Created and published by Knock Knock
Distributed by Who's There Inc.
Venice, CA 90291
knockknockstuff.com

ISBN: 978-160106451-6
UPC: 825703-50011-0

20 19 18 17 16 15 14 13 12 11 10 9 8 7 6 5 4 3 2

DINNER PARTY

Guest Book

KNOCK
KNOCK®
VENICE, CALIFORNIA

Memorable Moments: _____

_____

_____

_____

_____

_____

Additional Sentiments: _____

_____

_____

_____

_____

_____

Welcome to My Dinner Party

DATE OF PARTY: ....

TIME OF PARTY: .... AM / PM

MOVIE THAT BEST DESCRIBES THIS DINNER PARTY:

- ☐ *The Usual Suspects*
- ☐ *The Good, the Bad, and the Ugly*
- ☐ *Guess Who's Coming to Dinner*
- ☐ *Some Like It Hot*
- ☐ *Eat, Pray, Love*
- ☐ *As Good as It Gets*
- ☐ ....

PIE CHART

Shade and label the amount of time spent doing the following:

A. Eating   B. Drinking   C. Talking

D. ....

SIGN IN, PLEASE

| **TONIGHT WAS:** | ☐ Festive | ☐ Interesting | ☐ Relaxing |
| | ☐ Unpredictable | ☐ Over too soon | ☐ .... |

| **THE FOOD WAS:** | ☐ Adventurous | ☐ Scrumptious | ☐ Free |
| | ☐ Comforting | ☐ Unexpected | ☐ .... |

DINNER PLATE DOODLE

Draw the contents of your plate.

☐ Before eating   ☐ After eating

REASON FOR PARTY: ....

....

SEATED NEXT TO: ....

....

FAVORITE PHRASE OR OUTBURST:

" ....

....

....

"

REPORT CARD	A	B	C	D	F
Ambience					
Drinks					
Cuisine					
Conversation					
Décor					
Lighting					
Company					
OVERALL					

Memorable Moments: _____

_____

_____

_____

_____

_____

Additional Sentiments: _____

_____

_____

_____

_____

Welcome to My Dinner Party

DATE OF PARTY: ....

TIME OF PARTY: .... AM / PM

MOVIE THAT BEST DESCRIBES THIS DINNER PARTY:

- ☐ *The Usual Suspects*
- ☐ *The Good, the Bad, and the Ugly*
- ☐ *Guess Who's Coming to Dinner*
- ☐ *Some Like It Hot*
- ☐ *Eat, Pray, Love*
- ☐ *As Good as It Gets*
- ☐ ....

PIE CHART

Shade and label the amount of time spent doing the following:

A. Eating   B. Drinking   C. Talking

D. ....

SIGN IN, PLEASE

| TONIGHT WAS: | ☐ Festive | ☐ Interesting | ☐ Relaxing |
| | ☐ Unpredictable | ☐ Over too soon | ☐ .... |

| THE FOOD WAS: | ☐ Adventurous | ☐ Scrumptious | ☐ Free |
| | ☐ Comforting | ☐ Unexpected | ☐ .... |

DINNER PLATE DOODLE

Draw the contents of your plate.

☐ Before eating   ☐ After eating

REASON FOR PARTY: ....
....

SEATED NEXT TO: ....
....

FAVORITE PHRASE OR OUTBURST:

" ....

....

....

.... "

REPORT CARD	A	B	C	D	F
Ambience					
Drinks					
Cuisine					
Conversation					
Décor					
Lighting					
Company					
OVERALL					

Memorable Moments: _____
_____
_____
_____
_____

Additional Sentiments: _____
_____
_____
_____
_____

Welcome to My Dinner Party

DATE OF PARTY: ....

TIME OF PARTY: .... AM / PM

MOVIE THAT BEST DESCRIBES THIS DINNER PARTY:

- ☐ *The Usual Suspects*
- ☐ *The Good, the Bad, and the Ugly*
- ☐ *Guess Who's Coming to Dinner*
- ☐ *Some Like It Hot*
- ☐ *Eat, Pray, Love*
- ☐ *As Good as It Gets*
- ☐ ....

PIE CHART

Shade and label the amount of time spent doing the following:

A. Eating   B. Drinking   C. Talking

D. ....

SIGN IN, PLEASE

TONIGHT WAS:
- ☐ Festive
- ☐ Unpredictable
- ☐ Interesting
- ☐ Over too soon
- ☐ Relaxing
- ☐ ....

THE FOOD WAS:
- ☐ Adventurous
- ☐ Comforting
- ☐ Scrumptious
- ☐ Unexpected
- ☐ Free
- ☐ ....

DINNER PLATE DOODLE

Draw the contents of your plate.

☐ Before eating   ☐ After eating

REASON FOR PARTY: ....
....

SEATED NEXT TO: ....
....

FAVORITE PHRASE OR OUTBURST:

❝
....
....
....
....   ❞

REPORT CARD	A	B	C	D	F
Ambience					
Drinks					
Cuisine					
Conversation					
Décor					
Lighting					
Company					
OVERALL					

Memorable Moments: _____

_____

_____

_____

_____

_____

Additional Sentiments: _____

_____

_____

_____

_____

_____

Welcome to My Dinner Party

DATE OF PARTY: ....

TIME OF PARTY: .... AM / PM

MOVIE THAT BEST DESCRIBES THIS DINNER PARTY:

☐ The Usual Suspects
☐ The Good, the Bad, and the Ugly
☐ Guess Who's Coming to Dinner
☐ Some Like It Hot
☐ Eat, Pray, Love
☐ As Good as It Gets
☐ ....

PIE CHART
Shade and label the amount of time spent doing the following:

A. Eating   B. Drinking   C. Talking
D. ....

SIGN IN, PLEASE

| TONIGHT WAS: | ☐ Festive | ☐ Interesting | ☐ Relaxing |
| | ☐ Unpredictable | ☐ Over too soon | ☐ .... |

| THE FOOD WAS: | ☐ Adventurous | ☐ Scrumptious | ☐ Free |
| | ☐ Comforting | ☐ Unexpected | ☐ .... |

DINNER PLATE DOODLE
Draw the contents of your plate.

☐ Before eating   ☐ After eating

REASON FOR PARTY: ....
....

SEATED NEXT TO: ....
....

FAVORITE PHRASE OR OUTBURST:
"
....
....
....
....
                                                        "

REPORT CARD	A	B	C	D	F
Ambience					
Drinks					
Cuisine					
Conversation					
Décor					
Lighting					
Company					
OVERALL					

Memorable Moments: _____
_____
_____
_____
_____
_____

Additional Sentiments: _____
_____
_____
_____
_____
_____

Welcome to My Dinner Party

DATE OF PARTY: ....

TIME OF PARTY: .... AM / PM

MOVIE THAT BEST DESCRIBES THIS DINNER PARTY:

- ☐ *The Usual Suspects*
- ☐ *The Good, the Bad, and the Ugly*
- ☐ *Guess Who's Coming to Dinner*
- ☐ *Some Like It Hot*
- ☐ *Eat, Pray, Love*
- ☐ *As Good as It Gets*
- ☐ ....

PIE CHART

Shade and label the amount of time spent doing the following:

A. Eating   B. Drinking   C. Talking
D. ....

SIGN IN, PLEASE

TONIGHT WAS:
- ☐ Festive
- ☐ Unpredictable
- ☐ Interesting
- ☐ Over too soon
- ☐ Relaxing
- ☐ ....

THE FOOD WAS:
- ☐ Adventurous
- ☐ Comforting
- ☐ Scrumptious
- ☐ Unexpected
- ☐ Free
- ☐ ....

DINNER PLATE DOODLE

Draw the contents of your plate.

☐ Before eating   ☐ After eating

REASON FOR PARTY: ....
....

SEATED NEXT TO: ....
....

FAVORITE PHRASE OR OUTBURST:

66
....
....
....
....   99
....

REPORT CARD	A	B	C	D	F
Ambience					
Drinks					
Cuisine					
Conversation					
Décor					
Lighting					
Company					
OVERALL					

Memorable Moments: _____

_____

_____

_____

_____

Additional Sentiments: _____

_____

_____

_____

_____

Welcome to My Dinner Party

DATE OF PARTY: ....

TIME OF PARTY: .... AM / PM

MOVIE THAT BEST DESCRIBES THIS DINNER PARTY:

- ☐ The Usual Suspects
- ☐ The Good, the Bad, and the Ugly
- ☐ Guess Who's Coming to Dinner
- ☐ Some Like It Hot
- ☐ Eat, Pray, Love
- ☐ As Good as It Gets
- ☐ ....

PIE CHART

Shade and label the amount of time spent doing the following:

A. Eating   B. Drinking   C. Talking

D. ....

SIGN IN, PLEASE

| TONIGHT WAS: | ☐ Festive | ☐ Interesting | ☐ Relaxing |
| | ☐ Unpredictable | ☐ Over too soon | ☐ .... |

| THE FOOD WAS: | ☐ Adventurous | ☐ Scrumptious | ☐ Free |
| | ☐ Comforting | ☐ Unexpected | ☐ .... |

DINNER PLATE DOODLE

Draw the contents of your plate.

☐ Before eating   ☐ After eating

REASON FOR PARTY: ....

....

SEATED NEXT TO: ....

....

FAVORITE PHRASE OR OUTBURST:

"

....

....

....

"

REPORT CARD	A	B	C	D	F
Ambience					
Drinks					
Cuisine					
Conversation					
Décor					
Lighting					
Company					
OVERALL					

Memorable Moments: _____

_____

_____

_____

_____

Additional Sentiments: _____

_____

_____

_____

_____

Welcome to My Dinner Party

DATE OF PARTY: ....

TIME OF PARTY: .... AM / PM

MOVIE THAT BEST DESCRIBES THIS DINNER PARTY:

- ☐ *The Usual Suspects*
- ☐ *The Good, the Bad, and the Ugly*
- ☐ *Guess Who's Coming to Dinner*
- ☐ *Some Like It Hot*
- ☐ *Eat, Pray, Love*
- ☐ *As Good as It Gets*
- ☐ ....

PIE CHART

Shade and label the amount of time spent doing the following:

A. Eating   B. Drinking   C. Talking

D. ....

SIGN IN, PLEASE

| **TONIGHT WAS:** | ☐ Festive | ☐ Interesting | ☐ Relaxing |
| | ☐ Unpredictable | ☐ Over too soon | ☐ .... |

| **THE FOOD WAS:** | ☐ Adventurous | ☐ Scrumptious | ☐ Free |
| | ☐ Comforting | ☐ Unexpected | ☐ .... |

DINNER PLATE DOODLE

Draw the contents of your plate.

☐ Before eating   ☐ After eating

REASON FOR PARTY: ....
....

SEATED NEXT TO: ....
....

FAVORITE PHRASE OR OUTBURST:

" ....
....
....
....
.... "

REPORT CARD	A	B	C	D	F
Ambience					
Drinks					
Cuisine					
Conversation					
Décor					
Lighting					
Company					
OVERALL					

Memorable Moments: _____

_____

_____

_____

_____

_____

Additional Sentiments: _____

_____

_____

_____

_____

_____

Welcome to My Dinner Party

DATE OF PARTY: ....

TIME OF PARTY: .... AM / PM

MOVIE THAT BEST DESCRIBES THIS DINNER PARTY:

- ☐ *The Usual Suspects*
- ☐ *The Good, the Bad, and the Ugly*
- ☐ *Guess Who's Coming to Dinner*
- ☐ *Some Like It Hot*
- ☐ *Eat, Pray, Love*
- ☐ *As Good as It Gets*
- ☐ ....

PIE CHART
Shade and label the amount of time spent doing the following:

A. Eating   B. Drinking   C. Talking

D. ....

SIGN IN, PLEASE

| TONIGHT WAS: | ☐ Festive | ☐ Interesting | ☐ Relaxing |
| | ☐ Unpredictable | ☐ Over too soon | ☐ .... |

| THE FOOD WAS: | ☐ Adventurous | ☐ Scrumptious | ☐ Free |
| | ☐ Comforting | ☐ Unexpected | ☐ .... |

DINNER PLATE DOODLE
Draw the contents of your plate.

☐ Before eating   ☐ After eating

REASON FOR PARTY: ....
....

SEATED NEXT TO: ....
....

FAVORITE PHRASE OR OUTBURST:

" ....
....
....
....   "

REPORT CARD	A	B	C	D	F
Ambience					
Drinks					
Cuisine					
Conversation					
Décor					
Lighting					
Company					
OVERALL					

Memorable Moments: _____

_____

_____

_____

_____

_____

Additional Sentiments: _____

_____

_____

_____

_____

_____

Welcome to My Dinner Party

DATE OF PARTY: ....

TIME OF PARTY: .... AM / PM

MOVIE THAT BEST DESCRIBES THIS DINNER PARTY:

☐ The Usual Suspects
☐ The Good, the Bad, and the Ugly
☐ Guess Who's Coming to Dinner
☐ Some Like It Hot
☐ Eat, Pray, Love
☐ As Good as It Gets
☐ ....

PIE CHART

Shade and label the amount of time spent doing the following:

A. Eating   B. Drinking   C. Talking
D. ....

SIGN IN, PLEASE

| TONIGHT WAS: | ☐ Festive | ☐ Interesting | ☐ Relaxing |
| | ☐ Unpredictable | ☐ Over too soon | ☐ .... |

| THE FOOD WAS: | ☐ Adventurous | ☐ Scrumptious | ☐ Free |
| | ☐ Comforting | ☐ Unexpected | ☐ .... |

DINNER PLATE DOODLE
Draw the contents of your plate.

☐ Before eating   ☐ After eating

REASON FOR PARTY: ....
....

SEATED NEXT TO: ....
....

FAVORITE PHRASE OR OUTBURST:

"
....
....
....
....
"

REPORT CARD	A	B	C	D	F
Ambience					
Drinks					
Cuisine					
Conversation					
Décor					
Lighting					
Company					
OVERALL					

Memorable Moments: _____

_____

_____

_____

_____

_____

Additional Sentiments: _____

_____

_____

_____

_____

_____

Welcome to My Dinner Party

DATE OF PARTY: ....

TIME OF PARTY: .... AM / PM

MOVIE THAT BEST DESCRIBES THIS DINNER PARTY:

☐ *The Usual Suspects*
☐ *The Good, the Bad, and the Ugly*
☐ *Guess Who's Coming to Dinner*
☐ *Some Like It Hot*
☐ *Eat, Pray, Love*
☐ *As Good as It Gets*
☐ ....

PIE CHART
Shade and label the amount of time spent doing the following:

A. Eating   B. Drinking   C. Talking
D. ....

SIGN IN, PLEASE

TONIGHT WAS:	☐ Festive	☐ Interesting	☐ Relaxing
	☐ Unpredictable	☐ Over too soon	☐ ....
THE FOOD WAS:	☐ Adventurous	☐ Scrumptious	☐ Free
	☐ Comforting	☐ Unexpected	

DINNER PLATE DOODLE
Draw the contents of your plate.

☐ Before eating   ☐ After eating

REASON FOR PARTY: ....

....

SEATED NEXT TO: ....

FAVORITE PHRASE OR OUTBURST:

" ....

....

....

....

.... "

REPORT CARD	A	B	C	D	F
Ambience					
Drinks					
Cuisine					
Conversation					
Décor					
Lighting					
Company					
OVERALL					

Memorable Moments: _____

_____

_____

_____

_____

Additional Sentiments: _____

_____

_____

_____

_____

Welcome to My Dinner Party

DATE OF PARTY: ....

TIME OF PARTY: .... AM / PM

MOVIE THAT BEST DESCRIBES THIS DINNER PARTY:

☐ The Usual Suspects
☐ The Good, the Bad, and the Ugly
☐ Guess Who's Coming to Dinner
☐ Some Like It Hot
☐ Eat, Pray, Love
☐ As Good as It Gets
☐ ....

PIE CHART

Shade and label the amount of time spent doing the following:

A. Eating   B. Drinking   C. Talking
D. ....

SIGN IN, PLEASE

TONIGHT WAS:
☐ Festive   ☐ Interesting   ☐ Relaxing
☐ Unpredictable ☐ Over too soon   ☐ ....

THE FOOD WAS:
☐ Adventurous   ☐ Scrumptious   ☐ Free
☐ Comforting   ☐ Unexpected   ☐ ....

DINNER PLATE DOODLE

Draw the contents of your plate.

☐ Before eating   ☐ After eating

REASON FOR PARTY: ....
....

SEATED NEXT TO: ....

FAVORITE PHRASE OR OUTBURST:

"
....
....
....   "

REPORT CARD	A	B	C	D	F
Ambience					
Drinks					
Cuisine					
Conversation					
Décor					
Lighting					
Company					
OVERALL					

Memorable Moments: _____

_____

_____

_____

_____

Additional Sentiments: _____

_____

_____

_____

_____

Welcome to My Dinner Party

DATE OF PARTY: ....

TIME OF PARTY: .... AM / PM

MOVIE THAT BEST DESCRIBES THIS DINNER PARTY:

- ☐ *The Usual Suspects*
- ☐ *The Good, the Bad, and the Ugly*
- ☐ *Guess Who's Coming to Dinner*
- ☐ *Some Like It Hot*
- ☐ *Eat, Pray, Love*
- ☐ *As Good as It Gets*
- ☐ ....

PIE CHART

Shade and label the amount of time spent doing the following:

A. Eating   B. Drinking   C. Talking

D. ....

SIGN IN, PLEASE

TONIGHT WAS:
- ☐ Festive
- ☐ Unpredictable
- ☐ Interesting
- ☐ Over too soon
- ☐ Relaxing
- ☐ ....

THE FOOD WAS:
- ☐ Adventurous
- ☐ Comforting
- ☐ Scrumptious
- ☐ Unexpected
- ☐ Free
- ☐ ....

DINNER PLATE DOODLE

Draw the contents of your plate.

☐ Before eating   ☐ After eating

REASON FOR PARTY: ....

....

SEATED NEXT TO: ....

....

FAVORITE PHRASE OR OUTBURST:

66

....

....

.... 99

REPORT CARD	A	B	C	D	F
Ambience					
Drinks					
Cuisine					
Conversation					
Décor					
Lighting					
Company					
OVERALL					

Memorable Moments: _____

_____

_____

_____

_____

_____

Additional Sentiments: _____

_____

_____

_____

_____

Welcome to My Dinner Party

DATE OF PARTY: ....

TIME OF PARTY: .... AM / PM

MOVIE THAT BEST DESCRIBES THIS DINNER PARTY:

- ☐ *The Usual Suspects*
- ☐ *The Good, the Bad, and the Ugly*
- ☐ *Guess Who's Coming to Dinner*
- ☐ *Some Like It Hot*
- ☐ *Eat, Pray, Love*
- ☐ *As Good as It Gets*
- ☐ ....

PIE CHART

Shade and label the amount of time spent doing the following:

A. Eating   B. Drinking   C. Talking

D. ....

SIGN IN, PLEASE

TONIGHT WAS:
- ☐ Festive
- ☐ Unpredictable
- ☐ Interesting
- ☐ Over too soon
- ☐ Relaxing
- ☐ ....

THE FOOD WAS:
- ☐ Adventurous
- ☐ Comforting
- ☐ Scrumptious
- ☐ Unexpected
- ☐ Free
- ☐ ....

DINNER PLATE DOODLE

Draw the contents of your plate.

☐ Before eating   ☐ After eating

REASON FOR PARTY: ....

....

SEATED NEXT TO: ....

....

FAVORITE PHRASE OR OUTBURST:

" ....

....

....

.... "

REPORT CARD	A	B	C	D	F
Ambience					
Drinks					
Cuisine					
Conversation					
Décor					
Lighting					
Company					
OVERALL					

Memorable Moments: _____

_____

_____

_____

_____

_____

Additional Sentiments: _____

_____

_____

_____

_____

_____

Welcome to My Dinner Party

DATE OF PARTY: ....
TIME OF PARTY: .... AM / PM

MOVIE THAT BEST DESCRIBES THIS DINNER PARTY:

- ☐ The Usual Suspects
- ☐ The Good, the Bad, and the Ugly
- ☐ Guess Who's Coming to Dinner
- ☐ Some Like It Hot
- ☐ Eat, Pray, Love
- ☐ As Good as It Gets
- ☐ ....

PIE CHART

Shade and label the amount of time spent doing the following:

A. Eating   B. Drinking   C. Talking
D. ....

SIGN IN, PLEASE

TONIGHT WAS:
- ☐ Festive
- ☐ Unpredictable
- ☐ Interesting
- ☐ Over too soon
- ☐ Relaxing
- ☐ ....

THE FOOD WAS:
- ☐ Adventurous
- ☐ Comforting
- ☐ Scrumptious
- ☐ Unexpected
- ☐ Free
- ☐ ....

DINNER PLATE DOODLE

Draw the contents of your plate.

☐ Before eating   ☐ After eating

REASON FOR PARTY: ....
....

SEATED NEXT TO: ....
....

FAVORITE PHRASE OR OUTBURST:
66
....
....
....
....
                                        99

REPORT CARD	A	B	C	D	F
Ambience					
Drinks					
Cuisine					
Conversation					
Décor					
Lighting					
Company					
OVERALL					

Memorable Moments: _____

_____

_____

_____

_____

_____

Additional Sentiments: _____

_____

_____

_____

_____

Welcome to My Dinner Party

DATE OF PARTY: ....

TIME OF PARTY: .... AM / PM

MOVIE THAT BEST DESCRIBES THIS DINNER PARTY:

☐ The Usual Suspects
☐ The Good, the Bad, and the Ugly
☐ Guess Who's Coming to Dinner
☐ Some Like It Hot
☐ Eat, Pray, Love
☐ As Good as It Gets
☐ ....

PIE CHART
Shade and label the amount of time spent doing the following:

A. Eating   B. Drinking   C. Talking
D. ....

SIGN IN, PLEASE

| TONIGHT WAS: | ☐ Festive | ☐ Interesting | ☐ Relaxing |
| | ☐ Unpredictable | ☐ Over too soon | ☐ .... |

| THE FOOD WAS: | ☐ Adventurous | ☐ Scrumptious | ☐ Free |
| | ☐ Comforting | ☐ Unexpected | ☐ .... |

DINNER PLATE DOODLE
Draw the contents of your plate.

☐ Before eating   ☐ After eating

REASON FOR PARTY: ....

SEATED NEXT TO: ....

FAVORITE PHRASE OR OUTBURST:
"
....
....
....
                                    "

REPORT CARD	A	B	C	D	F
Ambience					
Drinks					
Cuisine					
Conversation					
Décor					
Lighting					
Company					
OVERALL					

Memorable Moments: _____

_____

_____

_____

_____

_____

Additional Sentiments: _____

_____

_____

_____

_____

_____

Welcome to My Dinner Party

DATE OF PARTY: ....

TIME OF PARTY: .... AM / PM

MOVIE THAT BEST DESCRIBES THIS DINNER PARTY:

- ☐ *The Usual Suspects*
- ☐ *The Good, the Bad, and the Ugly*
- ☐ *Guess Who's Coming to Dinner*
- ☐ *Some Like It Hot*
- ☐ *Eat, Pray, Love*
- ☐ *As Good as It Gets*
- ☐ ....

PIE CHART
Shade and label the amount of time spent doing the following:

A. Eating   B. Drinking   C. Talking

D. ....

SIGN IN, PLEASE

TONIGHT WAS:	☐ Festive	☐ Interesting	☐ Relaxing
	☐ Unpredictable	☐ Over too soon	☐ ....

THE FOOD WAS:	☐ Adventurous	☐ Scrumptious	☐ Free
	☐ Comforting	☐ Unexpected	☐ ....

DINNER PLATE DOODLE
Draw the contents of your plate.

☐ Before eating   ☐ After eating

REASON FOR PARTY: ....

....

SEATED NEXT TO: ....

....

FAVORITE PHRASE OR OUTBURST:

"
....
....
....
....
"

REPORT CARD	A	B	C	D	F
Ambience					
Drinks					
Cuisine					
Conversation					
Décor					
Lighting					
Company					
OVERALL					

Memorable Moments: _____
_____
_____
_____
_____
_____

Additional Sentiments: _____
_____
_____
_____
_____
_____

Welcome to My Dinner Party

DATE OF PARTY: ....

TIME OF PARTY: .... AM / PM

MOVIE THAT BEST DESCRIBES THIS DINNER PARTY:

- ☐ *The Usual Suspects*
- ☐ *The Good, the Bad, and the Ugly*
- ☐ *Guess Who's Coming to Dinner*
- ☐ *Some Like It Hot*
- ☐ *Eat, Pray, Love*
- ☐ *As Good as It Gets*
- ☐ ....

PIE CHART

Shade and label the amount of time spent doing the following:

A. Eating   B. Drinking   C. Talking

D. ....

SIGN IN, PLEASE

| **TONIGHT WAS:** | ☐ Festive | ☐ Interesting | ☐ Relaxing |
| | ☐ Unpredictable | ☐ Over too soon | ☐ .... |

| **THE FOOD WAS:** | ☐ Adventurous | ☐ Scrumptious | ☐ Free |
| | ☐ Comforting | ☐ Unexpected | ☐ .... |

DINNER PLATE DOODLE

Draw the contents of your plate.

☐ Before eating   ☐ After eating

REASON FOR PARTY: ....

....

SEATED NEXT TO: ....

FAVORITE PHRASE OR OUTBURST:

" ....

....

....

.... "

REPORT CARD	A	B	C	D	F
Ambience					
Drinks					
Cuisine					
Conversation					
Décor					
Lighting					
Company					
OVERALL					

Memorable Moments: _____

_____

_____

_____

_____

_____

Additional Sentiments: _____

_____

_____

_____

_____

_____

Welcome to My Dinner Party

DATE OF PARTY: ....

TIME OF PARTY: .... AM / PM

MOVIE THAT BEST DESCRIBES THIS DINNER PARTY:

☐ *The Usual Suspects*
☐ *The Good, the Bad, and the Ugly*
☐ *Guess Who's Coming to Dinner*
☐ *Some Like It Hot*
☐ *Eat, Pray, Love*
☐ *As Good as It Gets*
☐ ....

PIE CHART
Shade and label the amount of time spent doing the following:

A. Eating   B. Drinking   C. Talking
D. ....

SIGN IN, PLEASE

| TONIGHT WAS: | ☐ Festive | ☐ Interesting | ☐ Relaxing |
| | ☐ Unpredictable | ☐ Over too soon | ☐ .... |

| THE FOOD WAS: | ☐ Adventurous | ☐ Scrumptious | ☐ Free |
| | ☐ Comforting | ☐ Unexpected | ☐ .... |

DINNER PLATE DOODLE
Draw the contents of your plate.

☐ Before eating   ☐ After eating

REASON FOR PARTY: ....

SEATED NEXT TO: ....

FAVORITE PHRASE OR OUTBURST:
"
....
....
....
                                              "

REPORT CARD	A	B	C	D	F
Ambience					
Drinks					
Cuisine					
Conversation					
Décor					
Lighting					
Company					
OVERALL					

Memorable Moments: _____

_____

_____

_____

_____

Additional Sentiments: _____

_____

_____

_____

_____

Welcome to My Dinner Party

DATE OF PARTY: ....

TIME OF PARTY: .... AM / PM

MOVIE THAT BEST DESCRIBES THIS DINNER PARTY:

- ☐ *The Usual Suspects*
- ☐ *The Good, the Bad, and the Ugly*
- ☐ *Guess Who's Coming to Dinner*
- ☐ *Some Like It Hot*
- ☐ *Eat, Pray, Love*
- ☐ *As Good as It Gets*
- ☐ ....

PIE CHART

Shade and label the amount of time spent doing the following:

A. Eating   B. Drinking   C. Talking

D. ....

SIGN IN, PLEASE

TONIGHT WAS:
- ☐ Festive
- ☐ Unpredictable
- ☐ Interesting
- ☐ Over too soon
- ☐ Relaxing
- ☐ ....

THE FOOD WAS:
- ☐ Adventurous
- ☐ Comforting
- ☐ Scrumptious
- ☐ Unexpected
- ☐ Free
- ☐ ....

DINNER PLATE DOODLE

Draw the contents of your plate.

☐ Before eating   ☐ After eating

REASON FOR PARTY: ....

....

SEATED NEXT TO: ....

....

FAVORITE PHRASE OR OUTBURST:

" ....

....

....

....

...."

REPORT CARD	A	B	C	D	F
Ambience					
Drinks					
Cuisine					
Conversation					
Décor					
Lighting					
Company					
OVERALL					

Memorable Moments: _____

_____

_____

_____

_____

_____

Additional Sentiments: _____

_____

_____

_____

_____

_____

Welcome to My Dinner Party

DATE OF PARTY: ....

TIME OF PARTY: .... AM / PM

MOVIE THAT BEST DESCRIBES THIS DINNER PARTY:

- ☐ The Usual Suspects
- ☐ The Good, the Bad, and the Ugly
- ☐ Guess Who's Coming to Dinner
- ☐ Some Like It Hot
- ☐ Eat, Pray, Love
- ☐ As Good as It Gets
- ☐ ....

PIE CHART

Shade and label the amount of time spent doing the following:

A. Eating   B. Drinking   C. Talking

D. ....

SIGN IN, PLEASE

| **TONIGHT WAS:** | ☐ Festive | ☐ Interesting | ☐ Relaxing |
| | ☐ Unpredictable | ☐ Over too soon | ☐ .... |

| **THE FOOD WAS:** | ☐ Adventurous | ☐ Scrumptious | ☐ Free |
| | ☐ Comforting | ☐ Unexpected | ☐ .... |

DINNER PLATE DOODLE

Draw the contents of your plate.

☐ Before eating   ☐ After eating

REASON FOR PARTY: ....
....

SEATED NEXT TO: ....
....

FAVORITE PHRASE OR OUTBURST:

" ....
....
....
.... "

REPORT CARD	A	B	C	D	F
Ambience					
Drinks					
Cuisine					
Conversation					
Décor					
Lighting					
Company					
OVERALL					

Memorable Moments: _____

_____

_____

_____

_____

_____

Additional Sentiments: _____

_____

_____

_____

_____

_____

Welcome to My Dinner Party

DATE OF PARTY: ....
TIME OF PARTY: .... AM / PM

MOVIE THAT BEST DESCRIBES THIS DINNER PARTY:

☐ The Usual Suspects
☐ The Good, the Bad, and the Ugly
☐ Guess Who's Coming to Dinner
☐ Some Like It Hot
☐ Eat, Pray, Love
☐ As Good as It Gets
☐ ....

PIE CHART
Shade and label the amount of time spent doing the following:

A. Eating   B. Drinking   C. Talking
D. ....

SIGN IN, PLEASE

| **TONIGHT WAS:** | ☐ Festive | ☐ Interesting | ☐ Relaxing |
| | ☐ Unpredictable | ☐ Over too soon | ☐ .... |

| **THE FOOD WAS:** | ☐ Adventurous | ☐ Scrumptious | ☐ Free |
| | ☐ Comforting | ☐ Unexpected | ☐ .... |

DINNER PLATE DOODLE
Draw the contents of your plate.

☐ Before eating   ☐ After eating

REASON FOR PARTY: ....
....

SEATED NEXT TO: ....
....

FAVORITE PHRASE OR OUTBURST:
"
....
....
....
....
                                              "

REPORT CARD	A	B	C	D	F
Ambience					
Drinks					
Cuisine					
Conversation					
Décor					
Lighting					
Company					
OVERALL					

Memorable Moments: _____

_____

_____

_____

_____

Additional Sentiments: _____

_____

_____

_____

_____

Welcome to My Dinner Party

DATE OF PARTY: ....

TIME OF PARTY: .... AM / PM

MOVIE THAT BEST DESCRIBES THIS DINNER PARTY:

- ☐ The Usual Suspects
- ☐ The Good, the Bad, and the Ugly
- ☐ Guess Who's Coming to Dinner
- ☐ Some Like It Hot
- ☐ Eat, Pray, Love
- ☐ As Good as It Gets
- ☐ ....

PIE CHART

Shade and label the amount of time spent doing the following:

A. Eating   B. Drinking   C. Talking

D. ....

SIGN IN, PLEASE

| TONIGHT WAS: | ☐ Festive | ☐ Interesting | ☐ Relaxing |
| | ☐ Unpredictable | ☐ Over too soon | ☐ .... |

| THE FOOD WAS: | ☐ Adventurous | ☐ Scrumptious | ☐ Free |
| | ☐ Comforting | ☐ Unexpected | ☐ .... |

DINNER PLATE DOODLE

Draw the contents of your plate.

☐ Before eating   ☐ After eating

REASON FOR PARTY: ....

....

SEATED NEXT TO: ....

FAVORITE PHRASE OR OUTBURST:

"
....
....
....
....
"

REPORT CARD	A	B	C	D	F
Ambience					
Drinks					
Cuisine					
Conversation					
Décor					
Lighting					
Company					
OVERALL					

Memorable Moments: _____

_____

_____

_____

_____

_____

Additional Sentiments: _____

_____

_____

_____

_____

_____

Welcome to My Dinner Party

DATE OF PARTY: ....
TIME OF PARTY: .... AM / PM

MOVIE THAT BEST DESCRIBES THIS DINNER PARTY:

- ☐ *The Usual Suspects*
- ☐ *The Good, the Bad, and the Ugly*
- ☐ *Guess Who's Coming to Dinner*
- ☐ *Some Like It Hot*
- ☐ *Eat, Pray, Love*
- ☐ *As Good as It Gets*
- ☐ ....

PIE CHART
Shade and label the amount of time spent doing the following:

A. Eating   B. Drinking   C. Talking
D. ....

SIGN IN, PLEASE

| TONIGHT WAS: | ☐ Festive | ☐ Interesting | ☐ Relaxing |
| | ☐ Unpredictable | ☐ Over too soon | ☐ .... |

| THE FOOD WAS: | ☐ Adventurous | ☐ Scrumptious | ☐ Free |
| | ☐ Comforting | ☐ Unexpected | ☐ .... |

DINNER PLATE DOODLE
Draw the contents of your plate.

☐ Before eating   ☐ After eating

REASON FOR PARTY: ....
....

SEATED NEXT TO: ....
....

FAVORITE PHRASE OR OUTBURST:
"
....
....
....
"

REPORT CARD	A	B	C	D	F
Ambience					
Drinks					
Cuisine					
Conversation					
Décor					
Lighting					
Company					
OVERALL					

Memorable Moments: _____

_____

_____

_____

_____

_____

Additional Sentiments: _____

_____

_____

_____

_____

_____

Welcome to My Dinner Party

DATE OF PARTY: ....

TIME OF PARTY: .... AM / PM

MOVIE THAT BEST DESCRIBES THIS DINNER PARTY:

- ☐ The Usual Suspects
- ☐ The Good, the Bad, and the Ugly
- ☐ Guess Who's Coming to Dinner
- ☐ Some Like It Hot
- ☐ Eat, Pray, Love
- ☐ As Good as It Gets
- ☐ ....

PIE CHART
Shade and label the amount of time spent doing the following:

A. Eating   B. Drinking   C. Talking

D. ....

SIGN IN, PLEASE

| TONIGHT WAS: | ☐ Festive | ☐ Interesting | ☐ Relaxing |
| | ☐ Unpredictable | ☐ Over too soon | ☐ .... |

| THE FOOD WAS: | ☐ Adventurous | ☐ Scrumptious | ☐ Free |
| | ☐ Comforting | ☐ Unexpected | ☐ .... |

DINNER PLATE DOODLE
Draw the contents of your plate.

☐ Before eating   ☐ After eating

REASON FOR PARTY: ....
....

SEATED NEXT TO: ....
....

FAVORITE PHRASE OR OUTBURST:

"
....
....
....
....
 "

REPORT CARD	A	B	C	D	F
Ambience					
Drinks					
Cuisine					
Conversation					
Décor					
Lighting					
Company					
OVERALL					

Memorable Moments: _____

_____

_____

_____

_____

_____

Additional Sentiments: _____

_____

_____

_____

_____

_____

Welcome to My Dinner Party

DATE OF PARTY: ....
TIME OF PARTY: .... AM / PM

MOVIE THAT BEST DESCRIBES THIS DINNER PARTY:

- ☐ *The Usual Suspects*
- ☐ *The Good, the Bad, and the Ugly*
- ☐ *Guess Who's Coming to Dinner*
- ☐ *Some Like It Hot*
- ☐ *Eat, Pray, Love*
- ☐ *As Good as It Gets*
- ☐ ....

PIE CHART
Shade and label the amount of time spent doing the following:

A. Eating   B. Drinking   C. Talking
D. ....

SIGN IN, PLEASE

TONIGHT WAS:	☐ Festive	☐ Interesting	☐ Relaxing
	☐ Unpredictable	☐ Over too soon	☐ ....

THE FOOD WAS:	☐ Adventurous	☐ Scrumptious	☐ Free
	☐ Comforting	☐ Unexpected	☐ ....

DINNER PLATE DOODLE
Draw the contents of your plate.

☐ Before eating   ☐ After eating

REASON FOR PARTY: ....
....

SEATED NEXT TO: ....
....

FAVORITE PHRASE OR OUTBURST:
"
....
....
....
                                                    "

REPORT CARD	A	B	C	D	F
Ambience					
Drinks					
Cuisine					
Conversation					
Décor					
Lighting					
Company					
OVERALL					

Memorable Moments: _____
_____
_____
_____
_____
_____

Additional Sentiments: _____
_____
_____
_____
_____
_____

Welcome to My Dinner Party

DATE OF PARTY: ....

TIME OF PARTY: .... AM / PM

MOVIE THAT BEST DESCRIBES THIS DINNER PARTY:

☐ *The Usual Suspects*
☐ *The Good, the Bad, and the Ugly*
☐ *Guess Who's Coming to Dinner*
☐ *Some Like It Hot*
☐ *Eat, Pray, Love*
☐ *As Good as It Gets*
☐ ....

PIE CHART

Shade and label the amount of time spent doing the following:

A. Eating   B. Drinking   C. Talking
D. ....

SIGN IN, PLEASE

| TONIGHT WAS: | ☐ Festive | ☐ Interesting | ☐ Relaxing |
| | ☐ Unpredictable | ☐ Over too soon | ☐ .... |

| THE FOOD WAS: | ☐ Adventurous | ☐ Scrumptious | ☐ Free |
| | ☐ Comforting | ☐ Unexpected | ☐ .... |

DINNER PLATE DOODLE

Draw the contents of your plate.

☐ Before eating   ☐ After eating

REASON FOR PARTY: ....

SEATED NEXT TO: ....

FAVORITE PHRASE OR OUTBURST:

" ....
....
....
.... "

REPORT CARD	A	B	C	D	F
Ambience					
Drinks					
Cuisine					
Conversation					
Décor					
Lighting					
Company					
OVERALL					

Memorable Moments: _____

_____

_____

_____

_____

_____

Additional Sentiments: _____

_____

_____

_____

_____

_____

Welcome to My Dinner Party

DATE OF PARTY: ....

TIME OF PARTY: .... AM / PM

MOVIE THAT BEST DESCRIBES THIS DINNER PARTY:

☐ *The Usual Suspects*
☐ *The Good, the Bad, and the Ugly*
☐ *Guess Who's Coming to Dinner*
☐ *Some Like It Hot*
☐ *Eat, Pray, Love*
☐ *As Good as It Gets*
☐ ....

PIE CHART

Shade and label the amount of time spent doing the following:

A. Eating   B. Drinking   C. Talking
D. ....

SIGN IN, PLEASE

| TONIGHT WAS: | ☐ Festive | ☐ Interesting | ☐ Relaxing |
| | ☐ Unpredictable | ☐ Over too soon | ☐ .... |

| THE FOOD WAS: | ☐ Adventurous | ☐ Scrumptious | ☐ Free |
| | ☐ Comforting | ☐ Unexpected | ☐ .... |

DINNER PLATE DOODLE

Draw the contents of your plate.

☐ Before eating   ☐ After eating

REASON FOR PARTY: ....

SEATED NEXT TO: ....
....

FAVORITE PHRASE OR OUTBURST:

" ....
....
....
....   "

REPORT CARD	A	B	C	D	F
Ambience					
Drinks					
Cuisine					
Conversation					
Décor					
Lighting					
Company					
OVERALL					

Memorable Moments: _____
_____
_____
_____
_____
_____

Additional Sentiments: _____
_____
_____
_____
_____
_____

Welcome to My Dinner Party

DATE OF PARTY: ....

TIME OF PARTY: .... AM / PM

MOVIE THAT BEST DESCRIBES THIS DINNER PARTY:

☐ The Usual Suspects
☐ The Good, the Bad, and the Ugly
☐ Guess Who's Coming to Dinner
☐ Some Like It Hot
☐ Eat, Pray, Love
☐ As Good as It Gets
☐ ....

PIE CHART
Shade and label the amount of time spent doing the following:

A. Eating   B. Drinking   C. Talking
D. ....

SIGN IN, PLEASE

TONIGHT WAS:

☐ Festive   ☐ Interesting   ☐ Relaxing
☐ Unpredictable ☐ Over too soon   ☐ ....

THE FOOD WAS:

☐ Adventurous   ☐ Scrumptious   ☐ Free
☐ Comforting   ☐ Unexpected   ☐ ....

DINNER PLATE DOODLE
Draw the contents of your plate.

☐ Before eating   ☐ After eating

REASON FOR PARTY: ....
....

SEATED NEXT TO: ....
....

FAVORITE PHRASE OR OUTBURST:
66
....
....
....
....   99

REPORT CARD	A	B	C	D	F
Ambience					
Drinks					
Cuisine					
Conversation					
Décor					
Lighting					
Company					
OVERALL					

Memorable Moments: _____

_____

_____

_____

_____

_____

Additional Sentiments: _____

_____

_____

_____

_____

_____

Welcome to My Dinner Party

DATE OF PARTY: ....

TIME OF PARTY: .... AM / PM

MOVIE THAT BEST DESCRIBES THIS DINNER PARTY:

☐ *The Usual Suspects*
☐ *The Good, the Bad, and the Ugly*
☐ *Guess Who's Coming to Dinner*
☐ *Some Like It Hot*
☐ *Eat, Pray, Love*
☐ *As Good as It Gets*
☐ ....

PIE CHART

Shade and label the amount of time spent doing the following:

A. Eating   B. Drinking   C. Talking

D. ....

SIGN IN, PLEASE

| TONIGHT WAS: | ☐ Festive | ☐ Interesting | ☐ Relaxing |
| | ☐ Unpredictable | ☐ Over too soon | ☐ .... |

| THE FOOD WAS: | ☐ Adventurous | ☐ Scrumptious | ☐ Free |
| | ☐ Comforting | ☐ Unexpected | ☐ .... |

DINNER PLATE DOODLE

Draw the contents of your plate.

☐ Before eating   ☐ After eating

REASON FOR PARTY: ....

....

SEATED NEXT TO: ....

....

FAVORITE PHRASE OR OUTBURST:

" ....

....

....

.... "

REPORT CARD	A	B	C	D	F
Ambience					
Drinks					
Cuisine					
Conversation					
Décor					
Lighting					
Company					
OVERALL					

Memorable Moments: _____
_____
_____
_____
_____
_____

Additional Sentiments: _____
_____
_____
_____
_____
_____

Welcome to My Dinner Party

DATE OF PARTY: ....

TIME OF PARTY: ....AM / PM

MOVIE THAT BEST DESCRIBES THIS DINNER PARTY:

☐ *The Usual Suspects*
☐ *The Good, the Bad, and the Ugly*
☐ *Guess Who's Coming to Dinner*
☐ *Some Like It Hot*
☐ *Eat, Pray, Love*
☐ *As Good as It Gets*
☐ ....

PIE CHART

Shade and label the amount of time spent doing the following:

A. Eating   B. Drinking   C. Talking
D. ....

SIGN IN, PLEASE

| **TONIGHT WAS:** | ☐ Festive | ☐ Interesting | ☐ Relaxing |
| | ☐ Unpredictable | ☐ Over too soon | ☐ .... |

| **THE FOOD WAS:** | ☐ Adventurous | ☐ Scrumptious | ☐ Free |
| | ☐ Comforting | ☐ Unexpected | ☐ .... |

DINNER PLATE DOODLE

Draw the contents of your plate.

☐ Before eating   ☐ After eating

REASON FOR PARTY: ....

SEATED NEXT TO: ....

FAVORITE PHRASE OR OUTBURST:

" ....
....
....
.... "

REPORT CARD	A	B	C	D	F
Ambience					
Drinks					
Cuisine					
Conversation					
Décor					
Lighting					
Company					
OVERALL					

Memorable Moments: _____

_____

_____

_____

_____

Additional Sentiments: _____

_____

_____

_____

_____

Welcome to My Dinner Party

DATE OF PARTY: ....

TIME OF PARTY: .... AM / PM

MOVIE THAT BEST DESCRIBES THIS DINNER PARTY:

- ☐ *The Usual Suspects*
- ☐ *The Good, the Bad, and the Ugly*
- ☐ *Guess Who's Coming to Dinner*
- ☐ *Some Like It Hot*
- ☐ *Eat, Pray, Love*
- ☐ *As Good as It Gets*
- ☐ ....

PIE CHART

Shade and label the amount of time spent doing the following:

A. Eating   B. Drinking   C. Talking

D. ....

SIGN IN, PLEASE

TONIGHT WAS:
- ☐ Festive
- ☐ Unpredictable
- ☐ Interesting
- ☐ Over too soon
- ☐ Relaxing
- ☐ ....

THE FOOD WAS:
- ☐ Adventurous
- ☐ Comforting
- ☐ Scrumptious
- ☐ Unexpected
- ☐ Free
- ☐ ....

DINNER PLATE DOODLE

Draw the contents of your plate.

☐ Before eating   ☐ After eating

REASON FOR PARTY: ....

....

SEATED NEXT TO: ....

....

FAVORITE PHRASE OR OUTBURST:

" ....

....

....

.... "

REPORT CARD	A	B	C	D	F
Ambience					
Drinks					
Cuisine					
Conversation					
Décor					
Lighting					
Company					
OVERALL					

Memorable Moments: _____

_____

_____

_____

_____

_____

Additional Sentiments: _____

_____

_____

_____

_____

_____

Welcome to My Dinner Party

DATE OF PARTY: ....

TIME OF PARTY: .... AM / PM

MOVIE THAT BEST DESCRIBES THIS DINNER PARTY:

- ☐ The Usual Suspects
- ☐ The Good, the Bad, and the Ugly
- ☐ Guess Who's Coming to Dinner
- ☐ Some Like It Hot
- ☐ Eat, Pray, Love
- ☐ As Good as It Gets
- ☐ ....

PIE CHART

Shade and label the amount of time spent doing the following:

A. Eating   B. Drinking   C. Talking

D. ....

SIGN IN, PLEASE

TONIGHT WAS:
- ☐ Festive
- ☐ Unpredictable
- ☐ Interesting
- ☐ Over too soon
- ☐ Relaxing
- ☐ ....

THE FOOD WAS:
- ☐ Adventurous
- ☐ Comforting
- ☐ Scrumptious
- ☐ Unexpected
- ☐ Free
- ☐ ....

DINNER PLATE DOODLE

Draw the contents of your plate.

☐ Before eating   ☐ After eating

REASON FOR PARTY: ....
....

SEATED NEXT TO: ....
....

FAVORITE PHRASE OR OUTBURST:

" ....
....
....
....
                                          "

REPORT CARD	A	B	C	D	F
Ambience					
Drinks					
Cuisine					
Conversation					
Décor					
Lighting					
Company					
OVERALL					

Memorable Moments: _____

_____

_____

_____

_____

_____

Additional Sentiments: _____

_____

_____

_____

_____

_____

Welcome to My Dinner Party

DATE OF PARTY: ....

TIME OF PARTY: .... AM / PM

MOVIE THAT BEST DESCRIBES THIS DINNER PARTY:

☐ *The Usual Suspects*
☐ *The Good, the Bad, and the Ugly*
☐ *Guess Who's Coming to Dinner*
☐ *Some Like It Hot*
☐ *Eat, Pray, Love*
☐ *As Good as It Gets*
☐ ....

PIE CHART

Shade and label the amount of time spent doing the following:

A. Eating   B. Drinking   C. Talking
D. ....

SIGN IN, PLEASE

TONIGHT WAS:
☐ Festive   ☐ Interesting   ☐ Relaxing
☐ Unpredictable   ☐ Over too soon   ☐ ....

THE FOOD WAS:
☐ Adventurous   ☐ Scrumptious   ☐ Free
☐ Comforting   ☐ Unexpected   ☐ ....

DINNER PLATE DOODLE
Draw the contents of your plate.

☐ Before eating   ☐ After eating

REASON FOR PARTY: ....
....

SEATED NEXT TO: ....
....

FAVORITE PHRASE OR OUTBURST:

" ....
....
....
.... "

REPORT CARD	A	B	C	D	F
Ambience					
Drinks					
Cuisine					
Conversation					
Décor					
Lighting					
Company					
OVERALL					

Memorable Moments: _____

_____

_____

_____

_____

_____

Additional Sentiments: _____

_____

_____

_____

_____

_____

Welcome to My Dinner Party

DATE OF PARTY: ....

TIME OF PARTY: .... AM / PM

MOVIE THAT BEST DESCRIBES THIS DINNER PARTY:

☐ *The Usual Suspects*
☐ *The Good, the Bad, and the Ugly*
☐ *Guess Who's Coming to Dinner*
☐ *Some Like It Hot*
☐ *Eat, Pray, Love*
☐ *As Good as It Gets*
☐ ....

PIE CHART
Shade and label the amount of time spent doing the following:

A. Eating   B. Drinking   C. Talking
D. ....

SIGN IN, PLEASE

TONIGHT WAS:	☐ Festive	☐ Interesting	☐ Relaxing
	☐ Unpredictable	☐ Over too soon	☐ ....

THE FOOD WAS:	☐ Adventurous	☐ Scrumptious	☐ Free
	☐ Comforting	☐ Unexpected	☐ ....

DINNER PLATE DOODLE
Draw the contents of your plate.

☐ Before eating   ☐ After eating

REASON FOR PARTY: ....
....

SEATED NEXT TO: ....
....

FAVORITE PHRASE OR OUTBURST:
"
....
....
....
....
"

REPORT CARD	A	B	C	D	F
Ambience					
Drinks					
Cuisine					
Conversation					
Décor					
Lighting					
Company					
OVERALL					

Memorable Moments: _____
_____
_____
_____
_____

Additional Sentiments: _____
_____
_____
_____
_____

Welcome to My Dinner Party

DATE OF PARTY: ....

TIME OF PARTY: .... AM / PM

MOVIE THAT BEST DESCRIBES THIS DINNER PARTY:

☐ *The Usual Suspects*
☐ *The Good, the Bad, and the Ugly*
☐ *Guess Who's Coming to Dinner*
☐ *Some Like It Hot*
☐ *Eat, Pray, Love*
☐ *As Good as It Gets*
☐ ....

PIE CHART

Shade and label the amount of time spent doing the following:

A. Eating   B. Drinking   C. Talking
D. ....

SIGN IN, PLEASE

| TONIGHT WAS: | ☐ Festive | ☐ Interesting | ☐ Relaxing |
| | ☐ Unpredictable | ☐ Over too soon | ☐ .... |

| THE FOOD WAS: | ☐ Adventurous | ☐ Scrumptious | ☐ Free |
| | ☐ Comforting | ☐ Unexpected | ☐ .... |

DINNER PLATE DOODLE

Draw the contents of your plate.

☐ Before eating   ☐ After eating

REASON FOR PARTY: ....
....

SEATED NEXT TO: ....
....

FAVORITE PHRASE OR OUTBURST:

" ....
....
....
....
.... "

REPORT CARD	A	B	C	D	F
Ambience					
Drinks					
Cuisine					
Conversation					
Décor					
Lighting					
Company					
OVERALL					

Memorable Moments: _____

_____

_____

_____

_____

_____

Additional Sentiments: _____

_____

_____

_____

_____

_____

Welcome to My Dinner Party

DATE OF PARTY: ....

TIME OF PARTY: .... AM / PM

MOVIE THAT BEST DESCRIBES THIS DINNER PARTY:

☐ The Usual Suspects
☐ The Good, the Bad, and the Ugly
☐ Guess Who's Coming to Dinner
☐ Some Like It Hot
☐ Eat, Pray, Love
☐ As Good as It Gets
☐ ....

PIE CHART

Shade and label the amount of time spent doing the following:

A. Eating   B. Drinking   C. Talking
D. ....

SIGN IN, PLEASE

TONIGHT WAS:
☐ Festive   ☐ Interesting   ☐ Relaxing
☐ Unpredictable   ☐ Over too soon   ☐ ....

THE FOOD WAS:
☐ Adventurous   ☐ Scrumptious   ☐ Free
☐ Comforting   ☐ Unexpected   ☐ ....

DINNER PLATE DOODLE

Draw the contents of your plate.

☐ Before eating   ☐ After eating

REASON FOR PARTY: ....
....

SEATED NEXT TO: ....
....

FAVORITE PHRASE OR OUTBURST:

" ....
....
....
.... "

REPORT CARD	A	B	C	D	F
Ambience					
Drinks					
Cuisine					
Conversation					
Décor					
Lighting					
Company					
OVERALL					

Memorable Moments: _____

_____

_____

_____

_____

_____

Additional Sentiments: _____

_____

_____

_____

_____

_____

Welcome to My Dinner Party

DATE OF PARTY: ....

TIME OF PARTY: .... AM / PM

MOVIE THAT BEST DESCRIBES THIS DINNER PARTY:

- [ ] *The Usual Suspects*
- [ ] *The Good, the Bad, and the Ugly*
- [ ] *Guess Who's Coming to Dinner*
- [ ] *Some Like It Hot*
- [ ] *Eat, Pray, Love*
- [ ] *As Good as It Gets*
- [ ] ....

PIE CHART

Shade and label the amount of time spent doing the following:

A. Eating   B. Drinking   C. Talking

D. ....

SIGN IN, PLEASE

| TONIGHT WAS: | [ ] Festive | [ ] Interesting | [ ] Relaxing |
| | [ ] Unpredictable | [ ] Over too soon | [ ] .... |

| THE FOOD WAS: | [ ] Adventurous | [ ] Scrumptious | [ ] Free |
| | [ ] Comforting | [ ] Unexpected | [ ] .... |

DINNER PLATE DOODLE

Draw the contents of your plate.

[ ] Before eating   [ ] After eating

REASON FOR PARTY: ....

....

SEATED NEXT TO: ....

FAVORITE PHRASE OR OUTBURST:

“
....
....
....
....
”

REPORT CARD	A	B	C	D	F
Ambience					
Drinks					
Cuisine					
Conversation					
Décor					
Lighting					
Company					
OVERALL					

Memorable Moments: _____

_____

_____

_____

_____

_____

Additional Sentiments: _____

_____

_____

_____

_____

_____

Welcome to My Dinner Party

DATE OF PARTY: ....

TIME OF PARTY: .... AM / PM

MOVIE THAT BEST DESCRIBES THIS DINNER PARTY:

- ☐ *The Usual Suspects*
- ☐ *The Good, the Bad, and the Ugly*
- ☐ *Guess Who's Coming to Dinner*
- ☐ *Some Like It Hot*
- ☐ *Eat, Pray, Love*
- ☐ *As Good as It Gets*
- ☐ ....

PIE CHART

Shade and label the amount of time spent doing the following:

A. Eating   B. Drinking   C. Talking

D. ....

SIGN IN, PLEASE

| TONIGHT WAS: | ☐ Festive | ☐ Interesting | ☐ Relaxing |
| | ☐ Unpredictable | ☐ Over too soon | ☐ .... |

| THE FOOD WAS: | ☐ Adventurous | ☐ Scrumptious | ☐ Free |
| | ☐ Comforting | ☐ Unexpected | ☐ .... |

DINNER PLATE DOODLE

Draw the contents of your plate.

☐ Before eating   ☐ After eating

REASON FOR PARTY: ....
....

SEATED NEXT TO: ....
....

FAVORITE PHRASE OR OUTBURST:

" ....
....
.... "

REPORT CARD	A	B	C	D	F
Ambience					
Drinks					
Cuisine					
Conversation					
Décor					
Lighting					
Company					
OVERALL					

Memorable Moments: _____

_____

_____

_____

_____

Additional Sentiments: _____

_____

_____

_____

_____

Welcome to My Dinner Party

DATE OF PARTY: ....

TIME OF PARTY: .... AM / PM

MOVIE THAT BEST DESCRIBES THIS DINNER PARTY:

☐ The Usual Suspects
☐ The Good, the Bad, and the Ugly
☐ Guess Who's Coming to Dinner
☐ Some Like It Hot
☐ Eat, Pray, Love
☐ As Good as It Gets
☐ ....

PIE CHART

Shade and label the amount of time spent doing the following:

A. Eating   B. Drinking   C. Talking
D. ....

SIGN IN, PLEASE

| TONIGHT WAS: | ☐ Festive | ☐ Interesting | ☐ Relaxing |
| | ☐ Unpredictable | ☐ Over too soon | ☐ .... |

| THE FOOD WAS: | ☐ Adventurous | ☐ Scrumptious | ☐ Free |
| | ☐ Comforting | ☐ Unexpected | ☐ .... |

DINNER PLATE DOODLE

Draw the contents of your plate.

☐ Before eating   ☐ After eating

REASON FOR PARTY: ....

....

SEATED NEXT TO: ....

....

FAVORITE PHRASE OR OUTBURST:

" ....

....

....

"

REPORT CARD	A	B	C	D	F
Ambience					
Drinks					
Cuisine					
Conversation					
Décor					
Lighting					
Company					
OVERALL					

Memorable Moments: _____

_____

_____

_____

_____

Additional Sentiments: _____

_____

_____

_____

_____

Welcome to My Dinner Party

DATE OF PARTY: ....

TIME OF PARTY: .... AM / PM

MOVIE THAT BEST DESCRIBES THIS DINNER PARTY:

- ☐ *The Usual Suspects*
- ☐ *The Good, the Bad, and the Ugly*
- ☐ *Guess Who's Coming to Dinner*
- ☐ *Some Like It Hot*
- ☐ *Eat, Pray, Love*
- ☐ *As Good as It Gets*
- ☐ ....

PIE CHART

Shade and label the amount of time spent doing the following:

A. Eating   B. Drinking   C. Talking

D. ....

SIGN IN, PLEASE

| TONIGHT WAS: | ☐ Festive | ☐ Interesting | ☐ Relaxing |
| | ☐ Unpredictable | ☐ Over too soon | ☐ .... |

| THE FOOD WAS: | ☐ Adventurous | ☐ Scrumptious | ☐ Free |
| | ☐ Comforting | ☐ Unexpected | ☐ .... |

DINNER PLATE DOODLE

Draw the contents of your plate.

☐ Before eating   ☐ After eating

REASON FOR PARTY: ....

....

SEATED NEXT TO: ....

FAVORITE PHRASE OR OUTBURST:

"
....
....
....
....
"

REPORT CARD	A	B	C	D	F
Ambience					
Drinks					
Cuisine					
Conversation					
Décor					
Lighting					
Company					
OVERALL					

Memorable Moments: _____
_____
_____
_____
_____

Additional Sentiments: _____
_____
_____
_____
_____

Welcome to My Dinner Party

DATE OF PARTY: ....

TIME OF PARTY: .... AM / PM

MOVIE THAT BEST DESCRIBES THIS DINNER PARTY:

☐ *The Usual Suspects*
☐ *The Good, the Bad, and the Ugly*
☐ *Guess Who's Coming to Dinner*
☐ *Some Like It Hot*
☐ *Eat, Pray, Love*
☐ *As Good as It Gets*
☐ ....

PIE CHART

Shade and label the amount of time spent doing the following:

A. Eating   B. Drinking   C. Talking
D. ....

SIGN IN, PLEASE

| TONIGHT WAS: | ☐ Festive | ☐ Interesting | ☐ Relaxing |
| | ☐ Unpredictable | ☐ Over too soon | ☐ .... |

| THE FOOD WAS: | ☐ Adventurous | ☐ Scrumptious | ☐ Free |
| | ☐ Comforting | ☐ Unexpected | ☐ .... |

DINNER PLATE DOODLE
Draw the contents of your plate.

☐ Before eating   ☐ After eating

REASON FOR PARTY: ....
....

SEATED NEXT TO: ....
....

FAVORITE PHRASE OR OUTBURST:

" ....
....
....
....
....   "

REPORT CARD	A	B	C	D	F
Ambience					
Drinks					
Cuisine					
Conversation					
Décor					
Lighting					
Company					
OVERALL					

Memorable Moments: _____

_____

_____

_____

_____

Additional Sentiments: _____

_____

_____

_____

_____

Welcome to My Dinner Party

DATE OF PARTY: ....

TIME OF PARTY: .... AM / PM

MOVIE THAT BEST DESCRIBES THIS DINNER PARTY:

☐ *The Usual Suspects*
☐ *The Good, the Bad, and the Ugly*
☐ *Guess Who's Coming to Dinner*
☐ *Some Like It Hot*
☐ *Eat, Pray, Love*
☐ *As Good as It Gets*
☐ ....

PIE CHART

Shade and label the amount of time spent doing the following:

A. Eating   B. Drinking   C. Talking
D. ....

SIGN IN, PLEASE

TONIGHT WAS:
☐ Festive   ☐ Interesting   ☐ Relaxing
☐ Unpredictable   ☐ Over too soon   ☐ ....

THE FOOD WAS:
☐ Adventurous   ☐ Scrumptious   ☐ Free
☐ Comforting   ☐ Unexpected   ☐ ....

DINNER PLATE DOODLE

Draw the contents of your plate.

☐ Before eating   ☐ After eating

REASON FOR PARTY: ....

....

SEATED NEXT TO: ....

FAVORITE PHRASE OR OUTBURST:

" ....

....

....

....

.... "

REPORT CARD	A	B	C	D	F
Ambience					
Drinks					
Cuisine					
Conversation					
Décor					
Lighting					
Company					
OVERALL					

Memorable Moments: _____

_____

_____

_____

_____

_____

Additional Sentiments: _____

_____

_____

_____

_____

_____

Welcome to My Dinner Party

DATE OF PARTY: ....

TIME OF PARTY: .... AM / PM

MOVIE THAT BEST DESCRIBES THIS DINNER PARTY:

☐ The Usual Suspects
☐ The Good, the Bad, and the Ugly
☐ Guess Who's Coming to Dinner
☐ Some Like It Hot
☐ Eat, Pray, Love
☐ As Good as It Gets
☐ ....

PIE CHART

Shade and label the amount of time spent doing the following:

A. Eating   B. Drinking   C. Talking
D. ....

SIGN IN, PLEASE

| TONIGHT WAS: | ☐ Festive | ☐ Interesting | ☐ Relaxing |
| | ☐ Unpredictable | ☐ Over too soon | ☐ .... |

| THE FOOD WAS: | ☐ Adventurous | ☐ Scrumptious | ☐ Free |
| | ☐ Comforting | ☐ Unexpected | ☐ .... |

DINNER PLATE DOODLE

Draw the contents of your plate.

☐ Before eating   ☐ After eating

REASON FOR PARTY: ....

....

SEATED NEXT TO: ....

....

FAVORITE PHRASE OR OUTBURST:

"

....

....

....
                                            "

REPORT CARD	A	B	C	D	F
Ambience					
Drinks					
Cuisine					
Conversation					
Décor					
Lighting					
Company					
OVERALL					

Memorable Moments: _____

_____

_____

_____

_____

_____

Additional Sentiments: _____

_____

_____

_____

_____

_____

Welcome to My Dinner Party

DATE OF PARTY: ....

TIME OF PARTY: .... AM / PM

MOVIE THAT BEST DESCRIBES THIS DINNER PARTY:

☐ The Usual Suspects
☐ The Good, the Bad, and the Ugly
☐ Guess Who's Coming to Dinner
☐ Some Like It Hot
☐ Eat, Pray, Love
☐ As Good as It Gets
☐ ....

PIE CHART

Shade and label the amount of time spent doing the following:

A. Eating   B. Drinking   C. Talking
D. ....

SIGN IN, PLEASE

TONIGHT WAS:
☐ Festive   ☐ Interesting   ☐ Relaxing
☐ Unpredictable ☐ Over too soon   ☐ ....

THE FOOD WAS:
☐ Adventurous   ☐ Scrumptious   ☐ Free
☐ Comforting   ☐ Unexpected   ☐ ....

DINNER PLATE DOODLE

Draw the contents of your plate.

☐ Before eating   ☐ After eating

REASON FOR PARTY: ....
....

SEATED NEXT TO: ....
....

FAVORITE PHRASE OR OUTBURST:

" ....
....
....
....
.... "

REPORT CARD	A	B	C	D	F
Ambience					
Drinks					
Cuisine					
Conversation					
Décor					
Lighting					
Company					
OVERALL					

Memorable Moments: _____

_____

_____

_____

_____

Additional Sentiments: _____

_____

_____

_____

_____

Welcome to My Dinner Party

DATE OF PARTY: ....

TIME OF PARTY: .... AM / PM

MOVIE THAT BEST DESCRIBES THIS DINNER PARTY:

- ☐ The Usual Suspects
- ☐ The Good, the Bad, and the Ugly
- ☐ Guess Who's Coming to Dinner
- ☐ Some Like It Hot
- ☐ Eat, Pray, Love
- ☐ As Good as It Gets
- ☐ ....

PIE CHART

Shade and label the amount of time spent doing the following:

A. Eating   B. Drinking   C. Talking

D. ....

SIGN IN, PLEASE

TONIGHT WAS:
- ☐ Festive
- ☐ Unpredictable
- ☐ Interesting
- ☐ Over too soon
- ☐ Relaxing
- ☐ ....

THE FOOD WAS:
- ☐ Adventurous
- ☐ Comforting
- ☐ Scrumptious
- ☐ Unexpected
- ☐ Free
- ☐ ....

DINNER PLATE DOODLE
Draw the contents of your plate.

☐ Before eating   ☐ After eating

REASON FOR PARTY: ....
....

SEATED NEXT TO: ....
....

FAVORITE PHRASE OR OUTBURST:

"
....
....
....
....
                                              "

REPORT CARD	A	B	C	D	F
Ambience					
Drinks					
Cuisine					
Conversation					
Décor					
Lighting					
Company					
OVERALL					

Memorable Moments: _____

_____

_____

_____

_____

_____

Additional Sentiments: _____

_____

_____

_____

_____

_____

Welcome to My Dinner Party

DATE OF PARTY: ....

TIME OF PARTY: .... AM / PM

MOVIE THAT BEST DESCRIBES THIS DINNER PARTY:

- ☐ The Usual Suspects
- ☐ The Good, the Bad, and the Ugly
- ☐ Guess Who's Coming to Dinner
- ☐ Some Like It Hot
- ☐ Eat, Pray, Love
- ☐ As Good as It Gets
- ☐ ....

PIE CHART

Shade and label the amount of time spent doing the following:

A. Eating   B. Drinking   C. Talking

D. ....

SIGN IN, PLEASE

| **TONIGHT WAS:** | ☐ Festive | ☐ Interesting | ☐ Relaxing |
| | ☐ Unpredictable | ☐ Over too soon | ☐ .... |

| **THE FOOD WAS:** | ☐ Adventurous | ☐ Scrumptious | ☐ Free |
| | ☐ Comforting | ☐ Unexpected | ☐ .... |

DINNER PLATE DOODLE

Draw the contents of your plate.

☐ Before eating   ☐ After eating

REASON FOR PARTY: ....
....

SEATED NEXT TO: ....
....

FAVORITE PHRASE OR OUTBURST:

" ....
....
....
.... "

REPORT CARD	A	B	C	D	F
Ambience					
Drinks					
Cuisine					
Conversation					
Décor					
Lighting					
Company					
OVERALL					

Memorable Moments: _____

_____

_____

_____

_____

Additional Sentiments: _____

_____

_____

_____

_____

Welcome to My Dinner Party

DATE OF PARTY: ....
TIME OF PARTY: .... AM / PM

MOVIE THAT BEST DESCRIBES THIS DINNER PARTY:

☐ The Usual Suspects
☐ The Good, the Bad, and the Ugly
☐ Guess Who's Coming to Dinner
☐ Some Like It Hot
☐ Eat, Pray, Love
☐ As Good as It Gets
☐ ....

PIE CHART
Shade and label the amount of time spent doing the following:

A. Eating   B. Drinking   C. Talking
D. ....

SIGN IN, PLEASE

| TONIGHT WAS: | ☐ Festive | ☐ Interesting | ☐ Relaxing |
| | ☐ Unpredictable | ☐ Over too soon | ☐ .... |

| THE FOOD WAS: | ☐ Adventurous | ☐ Scrumptious | ☐ Free |
| | ☐ Comforting | ☐ Unexpected | ☐ .... |

DINNER PLATE DOODLE
Draw the contents of your plate.

☐ Before eating   ☐ After eating

REASON FOR PARTY: ....
....

SEATED NEXT TO: ....
....

FAVORITE PHRASE OR OUTBURST:
"
....
....
....
....
"

REPORT CARD	A	B	C	D	F
Ambience					
Drinks					
Cuisine					
Conversation					
Décor					
Lighting					
Company					
OVERALL					

Memorable Moments: _____

_____

_____

_____

_____

_____

Additional Sentiments: _____

_____

_____

_____

_____

_____

Welcome to My Dinner Party

DATE OF PARTY: ....

TIME OF PARTY: .... AM / PM

MOVIE THAT BEST DESCRIBES THIS DINNER PARTY:

- ☐ *The Usual Suspects*
- ☐ *The Good, the Bad, and the Ugly*
- ☐ *Guess Who's Coming to Dinner*
- ☐ *Some Like It Hot*
- ☐ *Eat, Pray, Love*
- ☐ *As Good as It Gets*
- ☐ ....

PIE CHART

Shade and label the amount of time spent doing the following:

A. Eating   B. Drinking   C. Talking

D. ....

SIGN IN, PLEASE

TONIGHT WAS:
- ☐ Festive
- ☐ Unpredictable
- ☐ Interesting
- ☐ Over too soon
- ☐ Relaxing
- ☐ ....

THE FOOD WAS:
- ☐ Adventurous
- ☐ Comforting
- ☐ Scrumptious
- ☐ Unexpected
- ☐ Free
- ☐ ....

DINNER PLATE DOODLE

Draw the contents of your plate.

☐ Before eating   ☐ After eating

REASON FOR PARTY: ....
....

SEATED NEXT TO: ....
....

FAVORITE PHRASE OR OUTBURST:

" ....
....
....
.... "

REPORT CARD	A	B	C	D	F
Ambience					
Drinks					
Cuisine					
Conversation					
Décor					
Lighting					
Company					
OVERALL					

Memorable Moments: _____

_____

_____

_____

_____

_____

Additional Sentiments: _____

_____

_____

_____

_____

_____

Welcome to My Dinner Party

DATE OF PARTY: ....

TIME OF PARTY: .... AM / PM

MOVIE THAT BEST DESCRIBES THIS DINNER PARTY:

- ☐ *The Usual Suspects*
- ☐ *The Good, the Bad, and the Ugly*
- ☐ *Guess Who's Coming to Dinner*
- ☐ *Some Like It Hot*
- ☐ *Eat, Pray, Love*
- ☐ *As Good as It Gets*
- ☐ ....

PIE CHART
Shade and label the amount of time spent doing the following:

A. Eating   B. Drinking   C. Talking
D. ....

SIGN IN, PLEASE

| TONIGHT WAS: | ☐ Festive | ☐ Interesting | ☐ Relaxing |
| | ☐ Unpredictable | ☐ Over too soon | ☐ .... |

| THE FOOD WAS: | ☐ Adventurous | ☐ Scrumptious | ☐ Free |
| | ☐ Comforting | ☐ Unexpected | ☐ .... |

DINNER PLATE DOODLE
Draw the contents of your plate.

☐ Before eating   ☐ After eating

REASON FOR PARTY: ....
....

SEATED NEXT TO: ....
....

FAVORITE PHRASE OR OUTBURST:

" ....
....
....
....
                                                          "

REPORT CARD	A	B	C	D	F
Ambience					
Drinks					
Cuisine					
Conversation					
Décor					
Lighting					
Company					
OVERALL					

Memorable Moments: _____

_____

_____

_____

_____

_____

Additional Sentiments: _____

_____

_____

_____

_____

_____

Welcome to My Dinner Party

DATE OF PARTY: ....

TIME OF PARTY: .... AM / PM

MOVIE THAT BEST DESCRIBES THIS DINNER PARTY:

☐ *The Usual Suspects*
☐ *The Good, the Bad, and the Ugly*
☐ *Guess Who's Coming to Dinner*
☐ *Some Like It Hot*
☐ *Eat, Pray, Love*
☐ *As Good as It Gets*
☐ ....

PIE CHART

Shade and label the amount of time spent doing the following:

A. Eating   B. Drinking   C. Talking
D. ....

SIGN IN, PLEASE

| TONIGHT WAS: | ☐ Festive | ☐ Interesting | ☐ Relaxing |
| | ☐ Unpredictable | ☐ Over too soon | ☐ .... |

| THE FOOD WAS: | ☐ Adventurous | ☐ Scrumptious | ☐ Free |
| | ☐ Comforting | ☐ Unexpected | ☐ .... |

DINNER PLATE DOODLE

Draw the contents of your plate.

☐ Before eating   ☐ After eating

REASON FOR PARTY: ....
....

SEATED NEXT TO: ....
....

FAVORITE PHRASE OR OUTBURST:

"
....
....
....
                                                "

REPORT CARD	A	B	C	D	F
Ambience					
Drinks					
Cuisine					
Conversation					
Décor					
Lighting					
Company					
OVERALL					

Memorable Moments: _____

_____

_____

_____

_____

_____

Additional Sentiments: _____

_____

_____

_____

_____

_____

Welcome to My Dinner Party

DATE OF PARTY: ....

TIME OF PARTY: .... AM / PM

MOVIE THAT BEST DESCRIBES THIS DINNER PARTY:

- ☐ *The Usual Suspects*
- ☐ *The Good, the Bad, and the Ugly*
- ☐ *Guess Who's Coming to Dinner*
- ☐ *Some Like It Hot*
- ☐ *Eat, Pray, Love*
- ☐ *As Good as It Gets*
- ☐ ....

PIE CHART

Shade and label the amount of time spent doing the following:

A. Eating   B. Drinking   C. Talking

D. ....

SIGN IN, PLEASE

| TONIGHT WAS: | ☐ Festive | ☐ Interesting | ☐ Relaxing |
| | ☐ Unpredictable | ☐ Over too soon | ☐ .... |

| THE FOOD WAS: | ☐ Adventurous | ☐ Scrumptious | ☐ Free |
| | ☐ Comforting | ☐ Unexpected | ☐ .... |

DINNER PLATE DOODLE

Draw the contents of your plate.

☐ Before eating   ☐ After eating

REASON FOR PARTY: ....
....

SEATED NEXT TO: ....

FAVORITE PHRASE OR OUTBURST:

"
....
....
....
....
                                                          "

REPORT CARD	A	B	C	D	F
Ambience					
Drinks					
Cuisine					
Conversation					
Décor					
Lighting					
Company					
OVERALL					

Memorable Moments: _____

_____

_____

_____

_____

_____

Additional Sentiments: _____

_____

_____

_____

_____

_____

Welcome to My Dinner Party

DATE OF PARTY: ....

TIME OF PARTY: .... AM / PM

MOVIE THAT BEST DESCRIBES THIS DINNER PARTY:

- ☐ *The Usual Suspects*
- ☐ *The Good, the Bad, and the Ugly*
- ☐ *Guess Who's Coming to Dinner*
- ☐ *Some Like It Hot*
- ☐ *Eat, Pray, Love*
- ☐ *As Good as It Gets*
- ☐ ....

PIE CHART

Shade and label the amount of time spent doing the following:

A. Eating   B. Drinking   C. Talking
D. ....

SIGN IN, PLEASE

TONIGHT WAS:
- ☐ Festive
- ☐ Unpredictable
- ☐ Interesting
- ☐ Over too soon
- ☐ Relaxing
- ☐ ....

THE FOOD WAS:
- ☐ Adventurous
- ☐ Comforting
- ☐ Scrumptious
- ☐ Unexpected
- ☐ Free
- ☐ ....

DINNER PLATE DOODLE
Draw the contents of your plate.

☐ Before eating   ☐ After eating

REASON FOR PARTY: ....

SEATED NEXT TO: ....

FAVORITE PHRASE OR OUTBURST:

"

....
....
....

"

REPORT CARD	A	B	C	D	F
Ambience					
Drinks					
Cuisine					
Conversation					
Décor					
Lighting					
Company					
OVERALL					

Memorable Moments: _____
_____
_____
_____
_____
_____

Additional Sentiments: _____
_____
_____
_____
_____
_____

Welcome to My Dinner Party

DATE OF PARTY: ....

TIME OF PARTY: .... AM / PM

MOVIE THAT BEST DESCRIBES THIS DINNER PARTY:

- ☐ *The Usual Suspects*
- ☐ *The Good, the Bad, and the Ugly*
- ☐ *Guess Who's Coming to Dinner*
- ☐ *Some Like It Hot*
- ☐ *Eat, Pray, Love*
- ☐ *As Good as It Gets*
- ☐ ....

PIE CHART
Shade and label the amount of time spent doing the following:

A. Eating   B. Drinking   C. Talking
D. ....

SIGN IN, PLEASE

TONIGHT WAS:
- ☐ Festive
- ☐ Unpredictable
- ☐ Interesting
- ☐ Over too soon
- ☐ Relaxing
- ☐ ....

THE FOOD WAS:
- ☐ Adventurous
- ☐ Comforting
- ☐ Scrumptious
- ☐ Unexpected
- ☐ Free
- ☐ ....

DINNER PLATE DOODLE
Draw the contents of your plate.

☐ Before eating   ☐ After eating

REASON FOR PARTY: ....
....

SEATED NEXT TO: ....
....

FAVORITE PHRASE OR OUTBURST:
66
....
....
....
....   99

REPORT CARD	A	B	C	D	F
Ambience					
Drinks					
Cuisine					
Conversation					
Décor					
Lighting					
Company					
OVERALL					

Memorable Moments: _____

_____

_____

_____

_____

Additional Sentiments: _____

_____

_____

_____

_____

Welcome to My Dinner Party

DATE OF PARTY: ....

TIME OF PARTY: .... AM / PM

MOVIE THAT BEST DESCRIBES THIS DINNER PARTY:

☐ *The Usual Suspects*
☐ *The Good, the Bad, and the Ugly*
☐ *Guess Who's Coming to Dinner*
☐ *Some Like It Hot*
☐ *Eat, Pray, Love*
☐ *As Good as It Gets*
☐ ....

PIE CHART

Shade and label the amount of time spent doing the following:

A. Eating   B. Drinking   C. Talking
D. ....

SIGN IN, PLEASE

| TONIGHT WAS: | ☐ Festive | ☐ Interesting | ☐ Relaxing |
| | ☐ Unpredictable | ☐ Over too soon | ☐ .... |

| THE FOOD WAS: | ☐ Adventurous | ☐ Scrumptious | ☐ Free |
| | ☐ Comforting | ☐ Unexpected | ☐ .... |

DINNER PLATE DOODLE

Draw the contents of your plate.

☐ Before eating   ☐ After eating

REASON FOR PARTY: ....
....

SEATED NEXT TO: ....
....

FAVORITE PHRASE OR OUTBURST:

" ....
....
.... "

REPORT CARD	A	B	C	D	F
Ambience					
Drinks					
Cuisine					
Conversation					
Décor					
Lighting					
Company					
OVERALL					

Memorable Moments: _____

_____

_____

_____

_____

_____

Additional Sentiments: _____

_____

_____

_____

_____

_____

Welcome to My Dinner Party

DATE OF PARTY: ....

TIME OF PARTY: .... AM / PM

MOVIE THAT BEST DESCRIBES THIS DINNER PARTY:

- ☐ The Usual Suspects
- ☐ The Good, the Bad, and the Ugly
- ☐ Guess Who's Coming to Dinner
- ☐ Some Like It Hot
- ☐ Eat, Pray, Love
- ☐ As Good as It Gets
- ☐ ....

PIE CHART

Shade and label the amount of time spent doing the following:

A. Eating   B. Drinking   C. Talking
D. ....

SIGN IN, PLEASE

| TONIGHT WAS: | ☐ Festive | ☐ Interesting | ☐ Relaxing |
| | ☐ Unpredictable | ☐ Over too soon | ☐ .... |

| THE FOOD WAS: | ☐ Adventurous | ☐ Scrumptious | ☐ Free |
| | ☐ Comforting | ☐ Unexpected | ☐ .... |

DINNER PLATE DOODLE

Draw the contents of your plate.

☐ Before eating   ☐ After eating

REASON FOR PARTY: ....
....

SEATED NEXT TO: ....
....

FAVORITE PHRASE OR OUTBURST:

❝
....
....
....
....   ❞

REPORT CARD	A	B	C	D	F
Ambience					
Drinks					
Cuisine					
Conversation					
Décor					
Lighting					
Company					
OVERALL					